TRANSITIONAL MATHEMATICS
Understanding Algebraic Expressions

ASSESSMENTS BOOK

John Woodward, Ph.D. and Mary Stroh, B.S.

Sopris West Educational Services • Longmont, Colorado

ISBN 1-59318-233-3

Edited by Louise Hutter Filipic
Editorial assistance by Annette Reaves
Text design by Edward Horcharik *and* Sebastian Pallini
Text production by Edward Horcharik *and* Matthew Williams
Cover design by Sue Campbell
Production assistance by Brenda Gagnon

07 06 05 04   6 5 4 3 2 1

Printed in the United States of America

Published and Distributed by

SOPRIS
WEST
EDUCATIONAL SERVICES

4093 Specialty Place • Longmont, Colorado 80504 • (800) 547-6747
www.sopriswest.com

ASSESSMENT
Test

Name _____ Date _____

PART 1
Write the following numbers in expanded form.

1. 1,039 = _____ + _____ + _____ + _____

2. 24,587 = _____ + _____ + _____ + _____ + _____

PART 2
Solve the following problems using expanded form. Show your work.

1.   678   → | | Answer ____
     + 223   + ____|_____|_____

2.   914   → | | Answer ____
     − 589   − ____|_____|_____

3. 897   → | | Answer ____
     × 6   × ____|_____|_____

PART 3

In each of the following division problems, start by pulling out the 10s. Then write the problem as a basic fact and solve it.

EXAMPLE $30\overline{)150}$ $3 \times 10\overline{)15 \times 10}$ $3\overline{)15}^{5}$ Answer: 5

1. $30\overline{)240}$ $\underline{\quad} \times 10\overline{)\underline{\quad} \times 10}$ $\overline{)\quad}$ Answer ____

2. $50\overline{)200}$ $\underline{\quad} \times 10\overline{)\underline{\quad} \times 10}$ $\overline{)\quad}$ Answer ____

PART 4

Solve the following basic and extended facts.

1. $9 + 8 =$ ____ $90 + 80 =$ ____ $900 + 800 =$ ____

2. $15 - 7 =$ ____ $150 - 70 =$ ____ $1,500 - 700 =$ ____

3. $6 \times 7 =$ ____ $60 \times 7 =$ ____ $600 \times 7 =$ ____

PART 5

Fill in the missing information in the following table. The first row is done for you.

Number	Ten (? × 10)	Hundred (? × 10 × 10)	Thousand (? × 10 × 10 × 10)
4,000	400 × 10	40 × 10 × 10	4 × 10 × 10 × 10
9,000			
8,000			
12,000			

PART 6

Write the following powers as repeated multiplication and then solve. You may use a calculator.

1. $3^3 \times 2^2 =$ _____

2. $2^5 \times 10^4 =$ _____

3. $10^8 =$ _____

4. $10^3 \times 2^2 \times 3^2 =$ _____

PART 7

Use PEMDAS to solve the following problems. Show each step.

1. $36 \div 4 \times 7 =$

2. $(12 - 2) - (3 + 2) =$

3. $3^2 \times (4 + 2) - 40 =$

4. $49 \div (5 + 2) \times 8 =$

ASSESSMENTS
Quiz

Name _____ Date _____

PART 1

Fill in the missing fractions and whole numbers on the following number lines.

1.
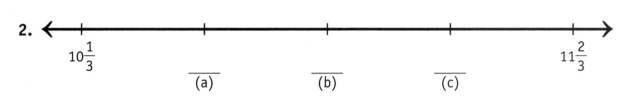

$\frac{1}{4}$　　$\frac{2}{4}$　　__(a)__　　__(b)__　　__(c)__

2.
$10\frac{1}{3}$　　__(a)__　　__(b)__　　__(c)__　　$11\frac{2}{3}$

PART 2

Solve the following addition and subtraction problems. Find a common denominator where one is needed.

1. $\frac{1}{2} + \frac{2}{6} =$ _____

2. $\frac{1}{3} + \frac{1}{3} =$ _____

3. $\frac{2}{5} - \frac{1}{5} =$ _____

4. $\frac{1}{6} - \frac{1}{9} =$ _____

PART 3
Solve the following problems by multiplying across.

1. $\dfrac{1}{3} \times \dfrac{1}{2} =$ —————— $=$ —

2. $\dfrac{1}{4} \times \dfrac{3}{5} =$ —————— $=$ —

3. $\dfrac{5}{9} \times \dfrac{1}{6} =$ —————— $=$ —

PART 4
Rewrite the following powers as repeated multiplications and then multiply across to solve the problems.

1. $\left(\dfrac{1}{4}\right)^2 =$ — $\times$ — $=$ —————— $=$ —

2. $\left(\dfrac{1}{3}\right)^2 =$ — $\times$ — $=$ —————— $=$ —

3. $\left(\dfrac{1}{2}\right)^4 =$ — $\times$ — $\times$ — $\times$ — $=$ ———————————— $=$ —

PART 5
Solve the following division problems by inverting and multiplying. Simplify your answers.

1. $\dfrac{2}{7} \div \dfrac{4}{2}$

The simplified answer is _____.

2. $\dfrac{4}{5} \div \dfrac{6}{4}$

The simplified answer is _____.

Name _____ Date _____

PART 1

Fill in the missing fractions, decimals, and percents on the following number line.

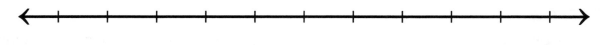

1. 0 $\dfrac{1}{5}$ $\dfrac{2}{5}$ ___(a)   ___(b)   ___(c)

2. 0   0.1   0.2   0.3   ___(a)   0.5   ___(b)   0.7   ___(c)   0.9   ___(d)

3. 0   10%   20%   30%   ___(a)   ___(b)   ___(c)   70%   ___(d)   90%   ___(e)

PART 2

Solve the following addition and subtraction problems. Find a common denominator where one is needed.

1. $\dfrac{1}{5} + \dfrac{2}{5} =$ ____

2. $\dfrac{1}{2} + \dfrac{1}{3} =$ ____

3. $\dfrac{4}{7} - \dfrac{3}{7} =$ ____

4. $\dfrac{5}{6} - \dfrac{4}{9} =$ ____

PART 3

Solve the following problems by multiplying across.

1. $\dfrac{1}{3} \times \dfrac{5}{4} =$ _____ $= —$

2. $\dfrac{1}{2} \times \dfrac{3}{5} =$ _____ $= —$

3. $\dfrac{1}{9} \times \dfrac{1}{8} =$ _____ $= —$

PART 4

Rewrite the following powers as repeated multiplications and then multiply across to solve the problems.

1. $\left(\dfrac{1}{5}\right)^2 = — \times — =$ _____ $= —$

2. $\left(\dfrac{1}{10}\right)^2 = — \times — =$ _____ $= —$

3. $\left(\dfrac{1}{3}\right)^4 = — \times — \times — \times — =$ _____ $= —$

PART 5

Solve the following division problems by inverting and multiplying. Simplify your answers.

1. $\dfrac{2}{5} \div \dfrac{8}{3}$

The simplified answer is _____.

2. $\dfrac{4}{5} \div \dfrac{1}{5}$

The simplified answer is _____.

PART 6

Convert the following fractions to decimals. You may use a calculator. Round the decimals to the nearest hundredths.

1. $\dfrac{1}{6} =$ _____

2. $\dfrac{4}{8} =$ _____

3. $\dfrac{7}{10} =$ _____

4. $\dfrac{5}{9} =$ _____

PART 7

Order the following decimals from smallest to largest.

1. 0.9, 0.19, 0.09, 0.1, 1.0, 0.99, 0.91

_____

2. 2.3, 2.02, 2.2, 2.33, 2.23, 2.03

_____

PART 8

Fill in the following table. The first row is done for you.

Fraction	Decimal	Percent
$\dfrac{1}{4}$	0.25	25%
$\dfrac{2}{100}$		
		80%
$\dfrac{3}{4}$		
	2.75	

PART 9

Solve the following percent problems. Remember to convert the percent to a decimal and then multiply. You may use a calculator.

1. Twenty-five percent (25%) of the students in the junior class attended the concert. There are 400 students in the junior class. How many students attended the concert?

2. Fifty percent (50%) of the city's radio stations are playing the New Band's newest song. There are 20 radio stations in that city. How many of them are playing the song?

PART 10

Use PEMDAS to solve the following problems involving fractions, decimals, and whole numbers. You may use a calculator. Show each step.

1. $\left(\dfrac{1}{2}\right)^2 + 2.25 \times 3 =$

2. $12 - \left(6.75 - \dfrac{3}{4}\right) =$

ASSESSMENT
Test

Name _____ Date _____

PART 1

Solve the following multiplication facts. Notice the missing part has been replaced with a variable. Write the correct answer over the top of the variable in the problem.

1. $8 \cdot 9 =$ ___m___

2. ___x___ $\cdot\ 7 = 56$

3. $6 \cdot$ ___t___ $= 42$

4. ___z___ $\cdot\ 5 = 45$

5. ___h___ $\cdot\ 9 = 27$

6. $8 \cdot 4 =$ ___v___

PART 2

Find the areas of the following rectangles. Use the formula: Area = l · w. Label your answer in square units.

1. 2

6

Area = _____

2. 5

3

Area = _____

3. 4

7

Area = _____

PART 3

Substitute the given value for the variable in each of the following problems. Then solve each problem.

1. If y = 9, what is the value of 4 · y?

4 · y = ?

↓ Substitute.

4 · ____ = ____

2. If z = 7, what is the value of z + 9?

z + 9 = ?

↓ Substitute.

____ + 9 = ____

3. If x = 8, what is the value of 12 − x?

12 − x = ?

↓ Substitute.

12 − ____ = ____

4. If w = 30, what is the value of w ÷ 5?

w ÷ 5 = ?

↓ Substitute.

____ ÷ 5 = ____

PART 4

Use PEMDAS and then guess and check *to solve the following problems. Use good number sense when choosing your guesses. You may use a calculator.*

1. (429 + 183) + x = 907

Answer: x = ____

2. (803 − 299) − z = 212

Answer: z = ____

PART 5

Use proportions to solve the following problems.

1. Jahintah painted one wall of her room pink. She used 2 small cans of red paint and 1 small can of white. She likes the color and wants to paint 3 more walls the same color. How much red and white paint should she use for the 3 walls?

Write a proportion that shows how much paint Jahintah needs to paint the 3 walls.

Answer _____ cans of red paint and _____ cans of white paint

2. Raynard is baking a cake for his mom's birthday. The recipe calls for 2 cups of sugar and 3 cups of flour. He is inviting a lot of people to the party so he decides to double the recipe. How much sugar and flour should he use in the recipe?

Write a proportion that shows how much sugar and flour Raynard needs for the bigger cake.

Answer _____ cups of sugar and _____ cups of flour

PART 6

Solve the following statements. (a) Choose a variable and state what it stands for. (b) Write the equation for the general pattern. (c) Solve for the specific example.

1. Toby is 3 years older than his sister Gina. Write an equation about Toby's age.

a. The variable _____ stands for _____.

b. Write the equation.

Toby's age = _____

c. Specific Example: When Gina is 9, Toby is _____ years old.

2. Everything in the store is on sale for 25% off. Write an equation to describe the discount.

   a. The variable _____ stands for _____.

   b. Write the equation here.

     Discount = _____

   c. Specific Example: What is the discount on a $200 DVD player? _____

3. You leave a 15% tip when you eat out at a restaurant. Write an equation to describe the tip.

   a. The variable _____ stands for _____.

   b. Write the equation.

     Tip = _____

   c. Specific Example: Suppose the lunch bill came to $25. How much will you leave

     for a tip? _____

4. Suppose you earned 2% interest on the money in your savings account. Write an equation.

   a. The variable _____ stands for _____.

   b. Write the equation.

     Interest = _____

   c. Specific Example: Suppose you have $879 in your account. How much interest

     will you earn? _____

PART 7

Use proportions to find distances between the following cities in miles. The key to the map is 1 inch = 50 miles.

Starting City	Ending City	Distance Between Cities (measured in inches on the map with a ruler)
City A	City B	3 inches
City C	City D	2 inches

1. Set up a proportion that shows the number of miles between City A and City B. What is the actual mileage between City A and City B?

   Answer: Distance in miles = _____

2. Set up a proportion that shows the number of miles between City C and City D. What is the actual mileage between City C and City D?

   Answer: Distance in miles = _____

ASSESSMENT
Test

Name _____ Date _____

PART 1
Write the following inequalities using words.

1. The inequality 34 > x means 34 is _____ *x.*

2. The inequality y < 29 means *y* is _____ 29.

3. The inequality w ≥ 100 means *w* is _____ 100.

4. The inequality 75 ≤ a means 75 is _____ *a.*

PART 2
Draw each of the following inequalities on the number line provided.

1. x > 80

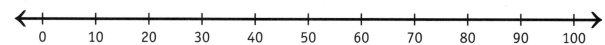

2. y < 50

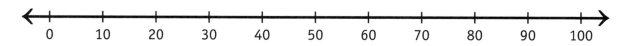

3. z ≥ 9

4. w ≤ 4

PART 3

Fill in the correct symbol (<, >, ≤, or ≥) in each of the following inequalities.

1. Barb is older than Kathryn. Kathryn is 13.

   B _____ 13

2. This month's phone bill will be at least as much as last month's phone bill. Last month's phone bill was $150.

   b _____ 150

3. The high temperature for today was 75 degrees.

   t _____ 75

4. The low temperature for today was 45 degrees.

   t _____ 45

PART 4

Solve the following word problems involving rates. Simplify the fractions if necessary.

1. Corina can run 6 miles in 54 minutes. *At this rate*, how long would it take her to run 2 miles?

   Answer _____

2. Maureen can do 25 sit-ups in 3 minutes. *At this rate*, how many sit-ups can she do in 6 minutes?

   Answer _____

3. Corey can practice the 5 songs for the concert in 15 minutes. *At this rate*, how long does it take him to practice one of the songs?

   Answer _____

PART 5

Draw each of the following double inequalities on the number lines provided.

1. $13 \geq x > 10$

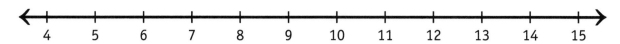

2. $79 \leq y < 85$

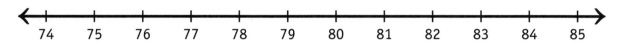

3. $127 > z > 124$

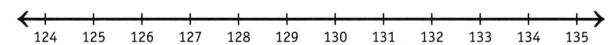

PART 6

Translate the following English words into double inequalities.

1. Becky can run the mile as fast as or faster than Tricia but not as fast as Julie. Tricia can run the mile in 10 minutes, and Julie can run the mile in 7 minutes. Use a double inequality to write this situation.

2. The high temperature for the day was 56 degrees and the low was 24 degrees. Use a double inequality to write this situation.

PART 7

Translate the following double inequalities into English words.

1. $5 < a < 12$, where a is someone's age in years

_____

_____

_____

_____

2. $125 < m < 375$, where m is money in dollars

_____

_____

_____

_____

Name _____   Date _____

PART 1

Fill in the opposite for each of the following numbers.

1. The opposite of 5 is _____.

2. The opposite of −32 is _____.

3. The opposite of −$\frac{1}{2}$ is _____.

4. The opposite of 75 is _____.

PART 2

Fill in the opposites on the following number lines.

1.
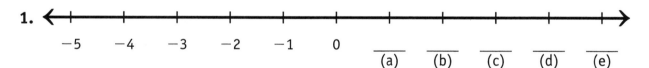

2.
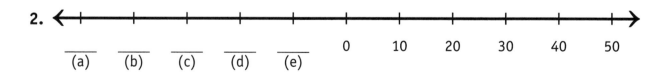

3.
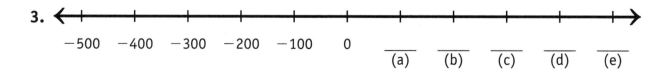

PART 3

Decide which of the two numbers in each of the following problems is bigger. Use the number line to help you. Fill in the inequality symbol ($<$ or $>$) that makes the statement true.

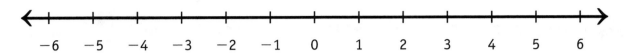

1. -2 _____ -3

2. -1 _____ -2

3. 2 _____ -5

4. -4 _____ 0

5. -3 _____ -4

6. -6 _____ -5

PART 4

Solve the following problems. Remember to rewrite the subtraction problems as addition problems by adding the opposite. Sketch a simple number line to help you.

1. $-4 - 3 = y$

   Rewrite the problem if necessary: _____

   Answer: $y = $ _____

2. $5 - -1 = x$

   Rewrite the problem if necessary: _____

   Answer: $x = $ _____

3. $-6 + 9 = z$

   Rewrite the problem if necessary: _____

   Answer: $z = $ _____

PART 5

Tell what equation is shown on each of the following number lines.

1.

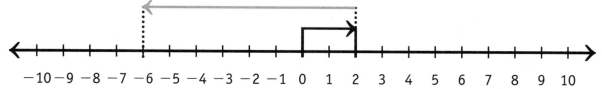

The equation is _____ + _____ = _____.

2.

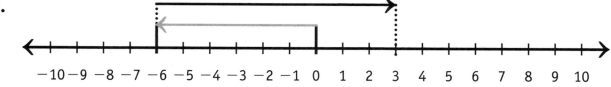

The equation is _____ + _____ = _____.

PART 6

Use the data from the following table to add dots to the dot graph. The first row of the table tells the time of day, and the second row tells how many hamburgers were sold at a local fast-food restaurant during each of the times listed.

Time of Day	Hamburgers Sold
10 A.M.–11 A.M.	25
11 A.M.–12 P.M.	38
12 P.M.–1 P.M.	65
1 P.M.–2 P.M.	45
2 P.M.–3 P.M.	33
3 P.M.–4 P.M.	41

Hourly Sales

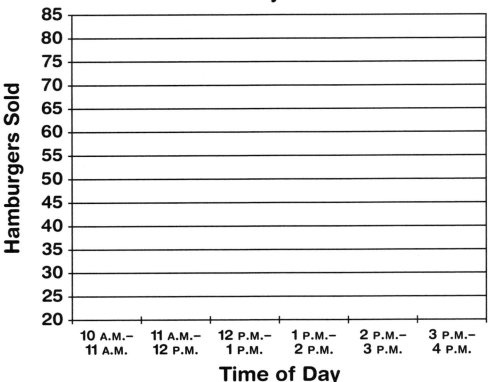

Hamburgers Sold (y-axis: 20, 25, 30, 35, 40, 45, 50, 55, 60, 65, 70, 75, 80, 85)

Time of Day (x-axis: 10 A.M.–11 A.M., 11 A.M.–12 P.M., 12 P.M.–1 P.M., 1 P.M.–2 P.M., 2 P.M.–3 P.M., 3 P.M.–4 P.M.)

1. During which hour were the most hamburgers sold? _____

2. During which hour were the least number of hamburgers sold? _____

3. What was the range in the number of hamburgers sold in one hour during the times listed? _____

4. Tell what decisions a manager of a fast-food restaurant might make based on the information in the graph.

   _____

   _____

   _____

ASSESSMENTS
Test

Name _____ Date _____

PART 1

Fill in the opposite for each of the following numbers.

1. The opposite of 150 is _____.

2. The opposite of −999 is _____.

3. The opposite of −275 is _____.

4. The opposite of 500 is _____.

PART 2

In each of the following problems, decide which number is bigger. Sketch a simple number line to help you. Then, for each problem fill in the inequality symbol (< or >) that makes the statement true.

1. −7 _____ −8

2. −5 _____ −4

3. 27 _____ −52

4. −40 _____ −30

5. −18 _____ −19

6. −600 _____ −500

PART 3

State what equation is shown by each of the following number lines.

1.

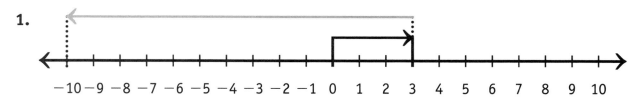

The equation is _____ + _____ = _____.

2.

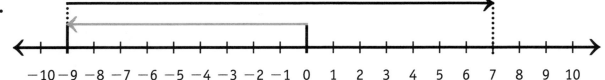

The equation is _____ + _____ = _____.

PART 4

Solve the following problems. Remember to rewrite the subtraction problems as addition problems by adding the opposite. If it helps you, sketch a simple number line.

1. $-42 - 37 = y$

Rewrite the problem if necessary: _____

Answer: $y =$ _____

2. $51 - -12 = x$

Rewrite the problem if necessary: _____

Answer: $x =$ _____

3. $-66 + 45 = z$

Rewrite the problem if necessary: _____

Answer: $z =$ _____

PART 5

Use the information in the following dot graph to answer the questions that follow. The information represents Janice's results on a five-question quiz. Each correct question is worth 10 points. If a question is answered incorrectly, 10 points are deducted from the score.

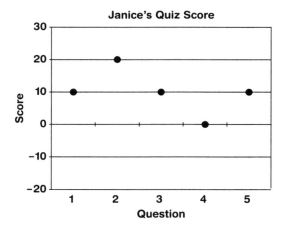

1. Which questions did Janice answer correctly? _____

2. Which questions did Janice answer incorrectly? _____

3. What was Janice's final score? _____

PART 6

Give the coordinates of the four points on the following coordinate graph.

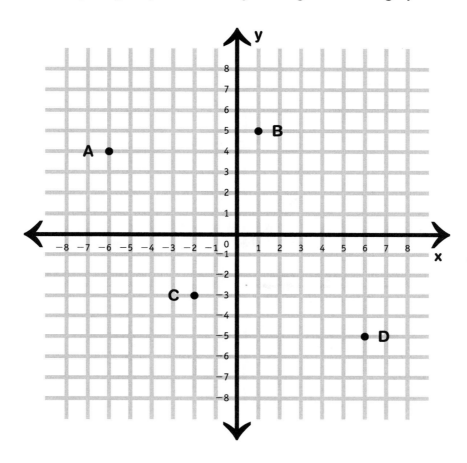

1. A = _____

2. B = _____

3. C = _____

4. D = _____

PART 7

Plot the given points on the following grid. Label each point with the letter and with the coordinates.

1. E = (1, 3)

2. F = (−3, 2)

3. G = (2, −2)

4. H = (−6, −1)

5. K = (6, 6)

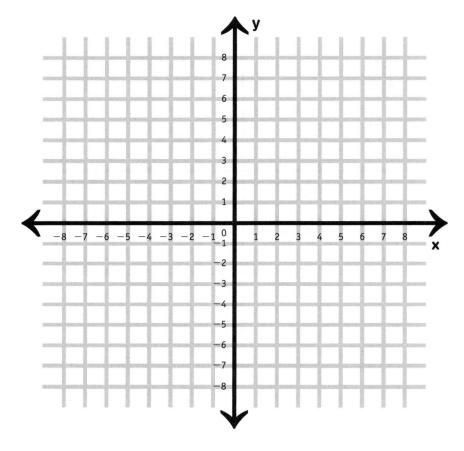

ASSESSMENT
Test

Name _____ Date _____

PART 1
Multiply the following positive and negative numbers. Remember to use the PASS rules.

1. $-7 \cdot -9 =$ _____

4. $5 \cdot -7 =$ _____

2. $-8 \cdot 6 =$ _____

5. $4 \cdot 8 =$ _____

3. $-3 \cdot -2 =$ _____

6. $-2 \cdot 9 =$ _____

PART 2
Divide the following positive and negative numbers. Remember to use the PASS rules.

1. $-64 \div 8 =$ _____

4. $-24 \div -6 =$ _____

2. $-7 \overline{)-42}$

5. $-9 \overline{)63}$

3. $\dfrac{20}{4} =$ _____

6. $\dfrac{27}{-3} =$ _____

PART 3

In each of the following expressions, substitute the value of the variable given. Then solve. Watch the signs carefully. Don't forget to use the PASS rules!

1. Expression: $-6 \cdot n$

Substitute -7 for n.

Answer _____

2. Expression: $8 \cdot m$

Substitute -9 for m.

Answer _____

3. Expression: $-49 \div x$

Substitute 7 for x.

Answer _____

4. Expression: $-81 \div z$

Substitute -9 for z.

Answer _____

PART 4

For each of following x/y tables, fill in the missing values. Then plot the lines on the coordinate graph provided. Label the lines Line A and Line B.

1. Line A: $y = x + 3$

x	y
2	
1	
0	
−1	
−2	

2. Line B: $y = 3 \cdot x$

x	y
2	
1	
0	
−1	
−2	

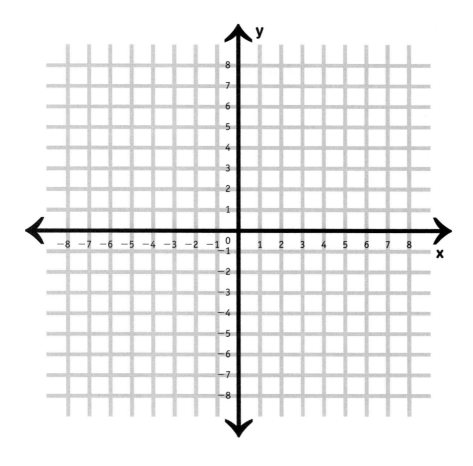

PART 5

Equations for two lines are given in each of the following problems. Decide whether the lines are intersecting lines or parallel lines. Circle the correct answer.

1. Line A: $y = 3 \cdot x$

Line B: $y = 3 \cdot x + 1$ Intersecting   or   Parallel

2. Line A: $y = 2 \cdot x + 7$

Line B: $y = x + 7$ Intersecting   or   Parallel

3. Line A: $y = 4 \cdot x$

Line B: $y = x + 4$ Intersecting   or   Parallel

4. Line A: $y = 3 \cdot x$

Line B: $y = 3 \cdot x + 3$ Intersecting   or   Parallel

PART 6

Give the (a) slope and (b) y-intercept for each of the following equations.

1. $y = x$

    a. The slope is _____.

    b. The *y*-intercept is _____.

2. $y = 3 \cdot x + 2$

    a. The slope is _____.

    b. The *y*-intercept is _____.

3. $y = 2 \cdot x + 1$

    a. The slope is _____.

    b. The *y*-intercept is _____.

4. $y = x + 7$

    a. The slope is _____.

    b. The *y*-intercept is _____.

ASSESSMENT
Test

Name _____ Date _____

PART 1
Rewrite the following multiplication problems as algebraic expressions with coefficients and variables.

$$2 \cdot a = 2a$$

EXAMPLE

1. $5 \cdot b =$ _____

2. $4 \cdot c =$ _____

3. $-2 \cdot d =$ _____

4. $-25 \cdot e =$ _____

PART 2
Write algebraic expressions for each of the following. Remember, negative symbols are written this way: ▼ ◼

1. ▼ ▼ + ◼ ◼ ◼

The algebraic expression is _____.

2. ▼ ▼ + ◼

The algebraic expression is _____.

3. ▼ ▼

The algebraic expression is _____.

PART 3

Evaluate the following simple expressions.

1. Evaluate 2x + 3 when x = 3.

Answer _____

2. Evaluate −3x + 5 when x = −3.

Answer _____

3. Evaluate x − 5 when x = 12.

Answer _____

PART 4

Decide if each of the following problems demonstrates the associative property or the commutative property. Circle the correct answer.

1. 3x + 7x + 2x

Rewritten: (3x + 7x) + 2x

ASSOCIATIVE PROPERTY   or   COMMUTATIVE PROPERTY

2. 2 + 3x + 5

Rewritten: 3x + 2 + 5

ASSOCIATIVE PROPERTY   or   COMMUTATIVE PROPERTY

3. 2x + 9 + 8x

Rewritten: 2x + 8x + 9

ASSOCIATIVE PROPERTY   or   COMMUTATIVE PROPERTY

PART 5

First simplify the expression and then evaluate for the given value of x. Show your work in the space provided.

1. Simplify $12 + 2x + 8 + 8x$. Evaluate when $x = -2$.

Simplify	Evaluate

2. Simplify $5x + 2 + -4x + -2$. Evaluate when $x = 5$.

Simplify	Evaluate

PART 6

Look at the pairs of objects in each of the following problems. Tell one thing that is the same and one thing that is different about the two objects.

1.

Figure A   Figure B

    a. What is one way that the objects are the same? _____

_____

    b. What is one way that the objects are different? _____

_____

2.

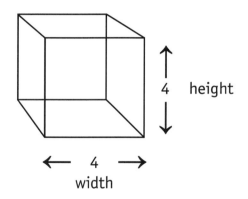

Figure C   Figure D

a. What is one way that the objects are the same? _____

_____

b. What is one way that the objects are different? _____

_____

PART 7

Calculate the surface area of the following cube. The area of one of its faces is 16 square units. Remember: Area of a square = height · width. There are six squares, or faces, on a cube, and all six faces are the same size.

4   height

4

width

Area of one face = 4 · 4 or 16 square units.

What is the surface area of the entire cube? _____

ASSESSMENTS
Quiz

Name _____ Date _____

PART 1

Rewrite the following subtraction problems as addition problems by adding the opposite. Then solve.

1. $2 - 9 =$ _____ = _____

2. $-1 - 7 =$ _____ = _____

3. $-4 - -3 =$ _____ = _____

PART 2

The following expressions all involve subtraction. Rewrite them as addition problems by adding the opposite.

1. $2x - 6 =$ _____

2. $x - -3 =$ _____

3. $-4x - 9 =$ _____

PART 3

Solve the following addition and subtraction problems involving decimal numbers. You may use a calculator.

1. $2.3 + 5.6 =$ _____

2. $-1.8 - -3.7 =$ _____

3. $-4.1 - 1.5 =$ _____

PART 4

Use rounding to get a ballpark answer for each of the following problems. Circle the best estimate from the choices given.

1. $18.1 - 2.5 + 14.9$

Circle the best estimate: -30 -10 10 30

2. $-5.5 - 1.9 - 2.1$

Circle the best estimate: -20 -10 10 20

PART 5

Simplify the following expressions. You may use a calculator.

1. $3x + 9.8 + 2x$

The simplified expression is _____.

2. $7 + 2.5x - 5$

The simplified expression is _____.

3. $3x + 4 + 1.5x + 3.7$

The simplified expression is _____.

4. $-2.5 - 1.6x + 5 + 2.6x$

The simplified expression is _____.

ASSESSMENTS
Test

Name _____ Date _____

PART 1
Rewrite the following subtraction problems as addition problems by adding the opposite. Then solve.

1. $2 - 3 =$ _____ = _____

2. $4 - -7 =$ _____ = _____

3. $-5 - 1 =$ _____ = _____

4. $-8 - -9 =$ _____ = _____

PART 2
The following expressions all involve subtraction. Rewrite them as addition by adding the opposite.

1. $x - 4 =$ _____

2. $-2x - 5 =$ _____

3. $3x - -6 =$ _____

4. $-7x - 9 =$ _____

PART 3
Solve the following addition and subtraction problems involving decimal numbers. You may use a calculator.

1. $2.5 + -1.4 =$ _____

2. $-1.6 - 5 =$ _____

3. $3.7 - -8 =$ _____

4. $-1.2 - -9.2 =$ _____

PART 4

Use rounding to get a ballpark answer for each of the following problems. Circle the best estimate from the choices given.

1. $4.5 + 19.9 - 5.2$

Circle the best estimate: -20 -5 5 20

2. $4.5 + 1.9 - 12.2$

Circle the best estimate: -20 -5 5 20

3. $-6.1 - 7.9 - 5.5$

Circle the best estimate: -20 -5 5 20

PART 5

Simplify the following expressions. You may use a calculator.

1. $3x + 1.9 - 2x$

The simplified expression is _____.

2. $4.5 + 2x + 2.1$

The simplified expression is _____.

3. $7.2x - 2.3 - 5.2x + 9.3$

The simplified expression is _____.

PART 6

Find the volume of each of the following objects. The formulas are given. Substitute the dimensions into the formula and solve. Remember, the units are cubic units—for example, in.³ You may use a calculator.

1. Find the volume of this cylinder. The formula is base · height.

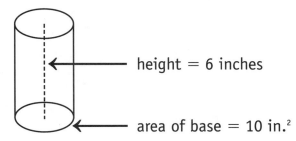

height = 6 inches

area of base = 10 in.²

Volume of cylinder = _____

2. Find the volume of this cone. The formula is $\frac{1}{3}$ · base · height.

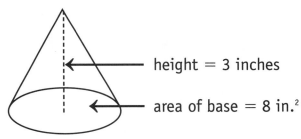

height = 3 inches

area of base = 8 in.²

Volume of cone = _____

ASSESSMENT QUIZ AND TEST ANSWER KEY

ASSESSMENT TEST ANSWER KEY

Unit 1 Test
PART 1
1. $1,000 + 0 + 30 + 9$
2. $20,000 + 4,000 + 500 + 80 + 7$

PART 2

1.
100	10	
600	70	8
+ 200	20	3
900	0	1

Answer: 901

2.
	100	
800	0	14
9̶0̶0̶	1̶0̶	4̶
− 500	80	9
300	20	5

Answer: 325

3.
800	90	7
×		6
		42
		540
+		4800
		5,382

Answer: 5,382

PART 3
Student responses are in bold type.

1. **3 × 10**$\overline{)24 \times 10}$ $3\overline{)24}$ ← **8**

   Answer: 8

2. **5 × 10**$\overline{)20 \times 10}$ $5\overline{)20}$ ← **4**

   Answer: 4

PART 4
1. 17   170   1,700
2. 8   80   800
3. 42   420   4,200

PART 5

Number	? × 10	? × 10 × 10	? × 10 × 10 × 10
4,000	400 × 10	40 × 10 × 10	4 × 10 × 10 × 10
9,000	**900 × 10**	**90 × 10 × 10**	**9 × 10 × 10 × 10**
8,000	**800 × 10**	**80 × 10 × 10**	**8 × 10 × 10 × 10**
12,000	**1,200 × 10**	**120 × 10 × 10**	**12 × 10 × 10 × 10**

Student responses are in bold type. Other information has already been filled in.

PART 6
1. $3 × 3 × 3 × 2 × 2 = 108$
2. $2 × 2 × 2 × 2 × 2 × 10 × 10 × 10 × 10 = 320,000$
3. $10 × 10 × 10 × 10 × 10 × 10 × 10 × 10 = 100,000,000$
4. $10 × 10 × 10 × 2 × 2 × 3 × 3 = 36,000$

PART 7

1. $36 \div 4 \times 7 =$
    $9 \times 7 = 63$

2. $(12 - 2) - (3 + 2) =$
    $10 - 5 = 5$

3. $3^2 \times (4 + 2) - 40 =$
    $3^2 \times 6 - 40 =$
    $9 \times 6 - 40 =$
    $54 - 40 = 14$

4. $49 \div (5 + 2) \times 8 =$
    $49 \div 7 \times 8 =$
    $7 \times 8 = 56$

ASSESSMENT QUIZ AND TEST ANSWER KEY

Unit 2 Quiz

PART 1

1. a. $\frac{3}{4}$
   b. 1
   c. $1\frac{1}{4}$

2. a. $10\frac{2}{3}$
   b. 11
   c. $11\frac{1}{3}$

PART 2

1. $\frac{3}{6} + \frac{2}{6} = \frac{5}{6}$

2. $\frac{2}{3}$

3. $\frac{1}{5}$

4. $\frac{3}{18} - \frac{2}{18} = \frac{1}{18}$

PART 3

1. $\frac{1 \times 1}{3 \times 2} = \frac{1}{6}$

2. $\frac{1 \times 3}{4 \times 5} = \frac{3}{20}$

3. $\frac{5 \times 1}{9 \times 6} = \frac{5}{54}$

PART 4

1. $\frac{1}{4} \times \frac{1}{4} = \frac{1 \times 1}{4 \times 4} = \frac{1}{16}$

2. $\frac{1}{3} \times \frac{1}{3} = \frac{1 \times 1}{3 \times 3} = \frac{1}{9}$

3. $\frac{1}{2} \times \frac{1}{2} \times \frac{1}{2} \times \frac{1}{2} = \frac{1 \times 1 \times 1 \times 1}{2 \times 2 \times 2 \times 2} = \frac{1}{16}$

PART 5

1. $\frac{2}{7} \times \frac{2}{4} = \frac{4}{28}$

   Simplified answer:

   $\frac{4}{28} = \frac{4}{4} \times \frac{1}{7} = \frac{1}{7}$

2. $\frac{4}{5} \times \frac{4}{6} = \frac{16}{30}$

   Simplified answer:

   $\frac{16}{30} = \frac{2}{2} \times \frac{8}{15} = \frac{8}{15}$

Unit 2 Test

PART 1

1. a. $\frac{3}{5}$
   b. $\frac{4}{5}$
   c. $\frac{5}{5}$ or 1

2. a. 0.4
   b. 0.6
   c. 0.8
   d. 1.0

3. a. 40%
   b. 50%
   c. 60%
   d. 80%
   e. 100%

PART 2

1. $\frac{3}{5}$

2. $\frac{5}{6}$

3. $\frac{1}{7}$

4. $\frac{7}{18}$

PART 3

1. $\frac{1 \times 5}{3 \times 4} = \frac{5}{12}$

2. $\frac{1 \times 3}{2 \times 5} = \frac{3}{10}$

3. $\frac{1 \times 1}{9 \times 8} = \frac{1}{72}$

PART 4

1. $\frac{1}{5} \times \frac{1}{5} = \frac{1 \times 1}{5 \times 5} = \frac{1}{25}$

2. $\frac{1}{10} \times \frac{1}{10} = \frac{1 \times 1}{10 \times 10} = \frac{1}{100}$

3. $\frac{1}{3} \times \frac{1}{3} \times \frac{1}{3} \times \frac{1}{3} = \frac{1 \times 1 \times 1 \times 1}{3 \times 3 \times 3 \times 3} = \frac{1}{81}$

PART 5

1. $\frac{2}{5} \times \frac{3}{8} = \frac{6}{40}$

   $\frac{6}{40} = \frac{2}{2} \times \frac{3}{20} = \frac{3}{20}$

2. $\frac{4}{5} \times \frac{5}{1} = \frac{20}{5}$

   $\frac{20}{5} = \frac{5}{5} \times \frac{4}{1} = \frac{4}{1} = 4$

PART 6

1. 0.17
2. 0.50
3. 0.70
4. 0.56

PART 7

1. 0.09, 0.1, 0.19, 0.9, 0.91, 0.99, 1.0

2. 2.02, 2.03, 2.2, 2.23, 2.3, 2.33

PART 8

Fraction	Decimal	Percent
$\frac{1}{4}$	0.25	25%
$\frac{2}{100}$	**0.02**	**2%**
$\frac{8}{10}$ or $\frac{80}{100}$	**0.8**	80%
$\frac{3}{4}$	**0.75**	**75%**
$\frac{275}{100}$	2.75	**275%**

Student responses are in bold type. The other information has already been filled in.

PART 9

1. $0.25 \times 400 = 100$; 100

2. $0.5 \times 20 = 10$; 10

PART 10

1. $\left(\frac{1}{2} \times \frac{1}{2}\right) + 2.25 \times 3 =$

$\frac{1}{4} + 2.25 \times 3 =$

$0.25 + 6.75 = 7$

2. $12 - (6.75 - 0.75) =$

$\qquad 12 - 6 = 6$

ASSESSMENT TEST ANSWER KEY

Unit 3 Test

PART 1

1. 72
2. 8
3. 7
4. 9
5. 3
6. 32

PART 2

1. 12 square units
2. 15 square units
3. 28 square units

PART 3

Student responses are in bold type. The other information is given.

1. $4 \cdot \mathbf{9} = \mathbf{36}$
2. $7 + 9 = \mathbf{16}$
3. $12 - \mathbf{8} = \mathbf{4}$
4. $\mathbf{30} \div 5 = \mathbf{6}$

PART 4

1. $x = 295$
2. $z = 292$

PART 5

1. $\dfrac{\text{Red paint}}{\text{White paint}}$ $\dfrac{2}{1} \cdot \dfrac{3}{3} = \dfrac{6}{3}$

   Answer: 6, 3

2. $\dfrac{\text{Sugar}}{\text{Flour}}$ $\dfrac{2}{3} \cdot \dfrac{2}{2} = \dfrac{4}{6}$

   Answer: 4, 6

PART 6

Students may choose any letters for the variables.

1. **a.** *G*, Gina's age
   b. Toby's age $= G + 3$
   c. 12
2. **a.** *c*, cost of item
   b. Discount $= 0.25 \cdot c$
   c. \$50
3. **a.** *b*, total of the bill
   b. Tip $= 0.15 \cdot b$
   c. \$3.75
4. **a.** *m*, money in account
   b. Interest $= 0.02 \cdot m$
   c. \$17.58

PART 7

1. $\dfrac{1}{50} \cdot \dfrac{3}{3} = \dfrac{3}{150}$

   Answer: 150

2. $\dfrac{1}{50} \cdot \dfrac{2}{2} = \dfrac{2}{100}$

   Answer: 100

ASSESSMENT TEST ANSWER KEY

Unit 4 Test

PART 1
1. greater than
2. less than
3. greater than or equal to
4. less than or equal to

PART 2
1.

A number line from 0 to 100 with an open circle at 80 and shading to the right.

2.

A number line from 0 to 100 with an open circle at 50 and shading to the left.

3.

A number line from 0 to 10 with a closed circle at 9 and shading to the right.

4.

A number line from 0 to 10 with a closed circle at 4 and shading to the left.

PART 3
1. $B > 13$
2. $b \geq 150$
3. $t \leq 75$
4. $t \geq 45$

PART 4
1. $\dfrac{\text{Miles}}{\text{Minutes}}$ $\dfrac{6}{54} = \dfrac{2}{x}$

    $\dfrac{\text{Miles}}{\text{Minutes}}$ $\dfrac{6}{54} = \dfrac{3}{3} \cdot \dfrac{2}{18}$

    Answer: $x = 18$ minutes

2. $\dfrac{\text{Sit-ups}}{\text{Minutes}}$ $\dfrac{25}{3} = \dfrac{x}{6}$

    $\dfrac{\text{Sit-ups}}{\text{Minutes}}$ $\dfrac{25}{3} \cdot \dfrac{2}{2} = \dfrac{50}{6}$

    Answer: $x = 50$ sit-ups

3. $\dfrac{\text{Songs}}{\text{Minute}}$ $\dfrac{5}{15} = \dfrac{1}{x}$

    $\dfrac{\text{Songs}}{\text{Minute}}$ $\dfrac{5}{15} = \dfrac{5}{5} \cdot \dfrac{1}{3}$

    Answer: $x = 3$ minutes

PART 5
1. $13 \geq x > 10$ looks like this on the number line.

A number line from 4 to 15 with an open circle at 10 and a closed circle at 13.

2. $79 \leq y < 85$ looks like this on the number line.

A number line from 74 to 85 with a closed circle at 79 and an open circle at 85.

3. $127 > z > 124$

A number line from 124 to 135 with open circles at 124 and 127.

PART 6
Students may choose any letters for the variables.
1. $7 < B \leq 10$
2. $24 \leq t \leq 56$

PART 7
Answers may vary. Sample answers:
1. Ben is 5 and Jerry is 12. Artie is older than Ben and younger than Jerry.
2. This month's phone bill is more than $125 but less than $375.

ASSESSMENT QUIZ AND TEST ANSWER KEY

Unit 5 Quiz
PART 1

1. -5
2. 32
3. $\frac{1}{2}$
4. -75

PART 2

1. **a.** 1
   b. 2
   c. 3
   d. 4
   e. 5
2. **a.** -50
   b. -40
   c. -30
   d. -20
   e. -10
3. **a.** 100
   b. 200
   c. 300
   d. 400
   e. 500

PART 3

1. >
2. >
3. >
4. <
5. >
6. <

PART 4

1. $-4 + -3 = -7; y = -7$
2. $5 + 1 = 6; x = 6$
3. Do not need to rewrite; $z = 3$

PART 5

1. $2 + -8 = -6$
2. $-6 + 9 = 3$

PART 6

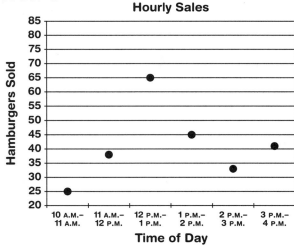

Hourly Sales

1. 12 P.M.–1 P.M.
2. 10 A.M.–11 A.M.
3. $65 - 25 = 40$

4. Answers will vary. Sample answers: The manager might decide to schedule more people to work from 12 P.M. to 1 P.M. The manager might use the information to schedule employees' lunch breaks. The manager might use the information to decide how many hamburgers to make up ahead of the "rush" time.

Unit 5 Test
PART 1

1. -150
2. 999
3. 275
4. -500

PART 2

1. >
2. <
3. >
4. <
5. >
6. <

PART 3

1. $3 + -13 = -10$
2. $-9 + 16 = 7$

PART 4

1. $-42 + -37 = y; y = -79$
2. $51 + 12 = x; x = 63$
3. Do not need to rewrite; $z = -21$

PART 5

1. 1, 2, and 5
2. 3 and 4
3. 10

PART 6

1. $A = (-6, 4)$
2. $B = (1, 5)$
3. $C = (-2, -3)$
4. $D = (6, -5)$

PART 7

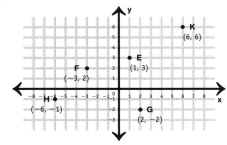

ASSESSMENT TEST ANSWER KEY

Unit 6 Test

PART 1
1. 63 **3.** 6 **5.** 32
2. −48 **4.** −35 **6.** −18

PART 2
1. −8 **3.** 5 **5.** −7
2. 6 **4.** 4 **6.** −9

PART 3
1. 42 **3.** −7
2. −72 **4.** 9

PART 4
Student responses are in bold type.
1. Line A: $y = x + 3$

x	y
2	5
1	4
0	3
−1	2
−2	1

2. Line B: $y = 3 \cdot x$

x	y
2	6
1	3
0	0
−1	−3
−2	−6

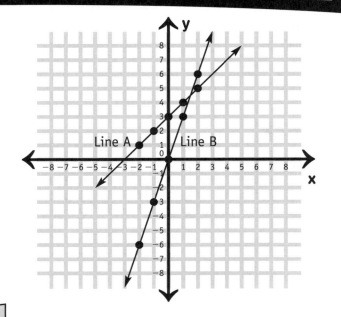

PART 5
1. parallel **3.** intersecting
2. intersecting **4.** parallel

PART 6
1. a. 1 **3. a.** 2
b. 0 **b.** 1
2. a. 3 **4. a.** 1
b. 2 **b.** 7

ASSESSMENT TEST ANSWER KEY

Unit 7 Test

PART 1

1. 5b
2. 4c
3. −2d
4. −25e

PART 2

1. $2x + -3$
2. $-2x + 1$
3. $2x$

PART 3

1. 9
2. 14
3. 7

PART 4

1. associative
2. commutative
3. commutative

PART 5

1. Simplify: $(2x + 8x) + (12 + 8)$
   10x + 20
   Evaluate: $10 \cdot -2 + 20$
   $-20 + 20$
   0
2. Simplify: $(5x + -4x) + (2 + -2)$
   x
   Evaluate: **5**

PART 6

Answers will vary. Sample answers:

1. **a.** Both figures have faces that meet at a point or vertex. Both figures have a base and a vertex.
   b. Figure A has one continuous curved face and a base. Figure B has four flat faces and a base. Figure A has a circle for the base and Figure B has a square. Figure A is called a cone and Figure B is called a pyramid.

2. **a.** Both figures have a top and a bottom that are parallel. If you drew lines from the top to the bottom, the lines would be parallel lines.
   b. Figure C has a circle for a base and Figure D has a rectangle. Figure C has one continuous curved face along with the top and bottom; and Figure D has four flat faces along with the top and bottom. Figure C is called a cylinder and Figure D is called a rectangular prism.

PART 7

Surface area $= 6 \cdot 16$, or 96 square units

ASSESSMENT QUIZ AND TEST ANSWER KEY

Unit 8 Quiz
PART 1
1. $2 + -9 = -7$
2. $-1 + -7 = -8$
3. $-4 + 3 = -1$

PART 2
1. $2x + -6$
2. $x + 3$
3. $-4x + -9$

PART 3
1. 7.9
2. 1.9
3. -5.6

PART 4
1. 30
2. -10

PART 5
1. $5x + 9.8$
2. $2.5x + 2$
3. $4.5x + 7.7$
4. $x + 2.5$

Unit 8 Test
PART 1
1. $2 + -3 = -1$
2. $4 + 7 = 11$
3. $-5 + -1 = -6$
4. $-8 + 9 = 1$

PART 2
1. $x + -4$
2. $-2x + -5$
3. $3x + 6$
4. $-7x + -9$

PART 3
1. 1.1
2. -6.6
3. 11.7
4. 8

PART 4
1. 20
2. -5
3. -20

PART 5
1. $x + 1.9$
2. $2x + 6.6$
3. $2x + 7$

PART 6
1. 60 in.^3
2. 8 in.^3